Never Shave a Camel

Never Shave a Camel

Dr Peter Rowan
Illustrated by Maggie Ling

JONATHAN CAPE
THIRTY-TWO BEDFORD SQUARE
LONDON

First published 1988
Text copyright © 1988 by Dr Peter Rowan
Illustrations copyright © 1988 by Maggie Ling
Jonathan Cape Ltd, 32 Bedford Square, London WC1B 3SG

A CIP catalogue record for this book is available from the British Library

ISBN 0 224 02607 0

Printed in Great Britain by
Mackays of Chatham PLC

For my daughter Sarah

Contents

Introduction

What should you do if a giant tarantula crawls up your leg? Or a king cobra bites? Could you drink sea water if you were cast adrift in a boat? What would happen if you were marooned on a desert island with only slugs to eat? Do you know where the East Indian puffer fish likes to bite? And why you should never shave a camel?

In 1985, after an expedition to the Antarctic, our ship "Discovery" sailed into Punta Arenas, Chile – the most southern port in the world.

I was sitting quietly in my cabin. Apart from someone from a nearby expedition breaking an arm, nothing serious had happened. We had survived all the ice and storms. After months I could relax!

Suddenly the captain put a call out for me. A crane unloading a fishing boat next to us had crashed into the dock. Our mooring ropes were just holding the cab above the waterline. Fuel from broken pipes was pouring over the driver trapped in the cab. And, as if that wasn't enough, some Korean fishermen were leaning over the crane and smoking!

That adventure had a happy ending. The man climbed out of the crane before the ropes broke. The cigarettes didn't blow us all up. And the TV and papers got some spectacular pictures ... A week later I was back home in England and found myself pulling a dying man out of a car crash just a few kilometres from my own house.

The world is a strange place. It can be full of adventures, whether you're on an Antarctic expedition, or simply relaxing in the school playground. Be prepared for emergencies and odd happenings. They come to all of us at some time. Usually when we're not expecting them!

9

What should you do if a king cobra bites you?

You could start praying. A lot of people think the king cobra is the deadliest snake in the world. You can't measure this sort of thing, but one expert has said that the "king" is the snake he would least like to be locked in a phone box with! Fortunately this type of cobra mainly lives in remote jungle areas where there are not many people (or phone boxes). So not too many people do meet it. Other snakes cause more deaths. The 40-centimetre-long carpet viper which lives in West Africa, the Middle East and India probably kills the most people in a year.

First aid for snake bite is not an easy subject – there are so very many different types of snake and different types of bite. I suppose the best advice is not to get bitten in the first place! The experts suggest keeping absolutely still if you are faced with a deadly snake because it is supposed to strike at moving things. This is easier said than done. I once trod on a cobra in the African bushland near the Zimbabwe/

South African border – and the only thing I remembered to do was jump.

If a poisonous snake does actually bite, some good general advice would be to keep as still and as quiet as possible. This helps stop the venom spreading around the body. People who have been bitten by a snake usually think they are going to die. They may be, but don't tell them that – fright and fear often do more harm than the snake. Tell them they are going to be fine. (Tell yourself if it's you that has been bitten.) Things will probably be all right, as most people do survive. After this get medical help quickly.

Most of the damage from a cobra bite comes because the venom damages the nerves that control the body's workings. If you are badly bitten it is painful but there are also problems like sweating, blurred vision, drooping eyelids, and difficulty in breathing, because these are all controlled by nerves. There are other members of the same snake family with this sort of venom as well as the cobras. These include the mambas, kraits, and coral snakes.

The other dangerous snakes are the vipers. These

include the true vipers like the European adder, and the pit vipers such as the rattlesnake, the fer-de-lance and the Malayan pit viper. Their venom acts differently from the cobras'. It breaks down blood cells and body tissues and this results in bleeding problems. This is not to say that the actual wound bleeds. What happens is that the venom damages the ability of the body to clot blood properly. The blood oozes out of its vessels into other tissues. This causes all sorts of problems ranging from bleeding gums to kidney failure.

One of the reasons it is difficult to give precise first aid advice for snake bites is that the snakes do not seem to have listened to the experts. They do not always inject what they are supposed to. The venom is often a mixture of the various damaging substances.

However, after a snake has struck it is often more important what you don't do than what you do do. Don't whip a penknife out and try to cut the bite away. This just causes more damage. Leave these sorts of heroics to Tarzan.

Using a tourniquet – something tight tied around the arm or leg – is also a method to avoid. Remember most bites are below the knee, so the idea is that something tied around here will stop the venom spreading up to the rest of the body. It's a good idea in theory, but in practice it nearly always isn't. It is very difficult to get the correct amount of pressure and it may make the damage worse. This is especially true after a bite which has stopped the blood clotting properly. The swelling that such a bite causes is made so much worse by a tourniquet that an arm or a leg can be lost. So do not tie anything tight like this.

Another remedy that is sometimes suggested is sucking the wound. (The old joke is that people who have been bitten on the backside will at least find out who their friends are before they die!) Not everyone agrees that sucking the bite helps. It may do. If you try this, spit any venom out. Personally I think washing the wound with water is just as effective.

There are many myths about snakes. However, some stories are true. For example, the African spitting cobra can hit a man's face with venom from several metres and this can temporarily blind. And rattlesnakes can "bite" after they are dead – even a severed head can do this – so it is good advice that you should never handle a dead snake.

Now the good news. There are nearly 3,000 sorts of snakes in the world and only 400 are poisonous. Even if you get bitten the snake will only be defending itself, so it will almost certainly not bother to give you a full dose of poison. Snakes mainly use venom to kill their food. Not only that but they will often warn you before biting – the rattlesnake shakes its tail and the cobra spreads the characteristic hood around its head.

So I know that snakes are not really dangerous. Now you know. Let's hope someone tells the snakes!

What happens if a centipede crawls up your nose?

Someone has to get it out! And you may be interested to know that this has actually happened in real life. It's best not to poke any "foreign body" (something in a place where it shouldn't be) up your nose. If an object such as a bead or wad of paper gets left there for more than a few days, you are likely to get a horrible green discharge down that side. As a matter of interest, foam rubber seems to give the most revolting of all discharges.

Don't try and get the object out yourself – you may do more harm than good. It's best to get help. Doctors have special instruments for lighting up the inside of the nose and grabbing whatever shouldn't be there.

Some amazing things have been removed from noses. One doctor's newspaper I read recently reported objects as varied as thimbles, knife blades and flies. They weren't all in the same nose, you understand. Although an Englishman called Thomas Wedders who lived in Yorkshire in the early eighteenth century had enough room. His nose – at over 20 centimetres – is the largest on record.

The ear is a fairly common place to find insects. (The earwig's name comes from the belief that it could get inside your head by creeping into your ear if you fell asleep outside on the ground.) I know of one lady who complained of a buzzing in her head. It took some time to discover that this was coming from a live fly trapped down near the eardrum. This would be quite an unpleasant feeling. The saying "to send someone away with a flea in his ear" means to dismiss someone with a telling off. It comes from the fact that a dog with an insect inside its ear is restless and frightened and will run away in fear.

Quite recently a 75-year-old man who had been deaf most of his life – a Mr Jack Cracker to be precise – got a sweet stuck in his throat. Mrs Cracker, his wife, thumped him on the back to get it out. (Quite a good move.) However, to everyone's surprise, a rolled-up bus ticket shot out of his ear as well. This ticket was dated 2 May 1927. Mr Cracker realised he must have pushed this into his ear 60 years previously. It had been blocking his ear most of his life.

And unusual things sometimes find their way accidentally or deliberately into other parts of the body. Even the belly button gets misused like this. Despite what some people may say, it is not for keeping the salt in when you eat celery in the bath.

Could a vampire sink its teeth into your neck while you are asleep?

Yes, but you would be very unlucky if this happened to you. Human vampires are fortunately few and far between. The original one was a fifteenth-century prince in Rumania, called Dracula. His Dad was called Vlad Drakul which means "the Devil" – he is remembered as "The Impaler" because he stuck his enemies on stakes. (In 1897 a novel was written about a count who wore a cape and drank the blood of pretty girls! This is only a story.) There is, however, a small South American vampire bat, about 10 centimetres long, which uses its needle-sharp front teeth to bite the neck and then laps up blood. It usually goes for animals such as cows, horses and goats but it will bite humans. It can deaden the pain of the bite so you do not feel the teeth. This means it can feed on you while you are asleep.

There is no doubt that the main problem of vampire bats is that they carry rabies. (In Latin America up to a million head of cattle are lost every year because of rabies spread by vampire bats. It has been worked out from this that the loss in money terms is a staggering $100 million per year!) Anyway, rabies is an infection which can also kill humans. It is usually spread to us by the bite of dogs, cats, bats and foxes. If you catch it and you drink water your throat could seize up. This brings an indescribable feeling of terror. Another name for rabies, "hydrophobia", literally means fear of water.

So you should beware of being bitten by animals, vampires included, in areas where there is rabies. And if you are bitten by the dreaded "mad dog", clean the wound and get help fast. (Animals with rabies go "mad" because the bullet-shaped virus damages the brain.) Also, do not smuggle animals from areas where there is rabies into countries which do not yet have the disease – even if an animal seems perfectly healthy, it may well be infected. In one recent survey, 64 of the world's countries had rabies and 26 reported they did not. Once it's in a country, it's very difficult to stop it spreading.

Although you are very unlikely to meet either a bat or a human vampire, there are some peculiar people in the world who may or may not be after your blood. So you must be really careful of talking to strangers. You can never be sure about them. And do not let them trick you. A favourite ploy is to ask you to get into their car. They always seem very nice at first. They may even know your name or pretend to be a friend of your Mum or Dad. Tell your parents if you meet anyone like this.

It really is tricky for everyone having "oddballs" about. Not long ago I was travelling on an Underground train in London when two young girls recognised me from being on the television. They came across for a chat without telling their mother. She was looking the other way.

I chatted to them for a few minutes, and they asked for some pictures and autographs which I did not have with me. I said I would send them if they told me where they lived. Just at this moment the girls' mother looked around and rushed over looking horrified. Before I could say anything the train doors were open and she had rushed them off into the crowd. I knew what she was thinking. But in the noise and bustle of the train I had not been able to explain.

What happens if a tarantula crawls up your leg?

Probably not a lot. The big hairy creatures you often see in pet shops, which most people think of as tarantulas, do not often bite. They cause most trouble by frightening people and by what they do with their back legs. If you upset one it rubs its legs on a circular hairy patch on its belly. This sets up a fine mist of broken hairs which can be very irritating to the eyes and skin.

In fact these "tarantulas" are not even called true spiders by the experts. They are commonly known as bird-eating spiders because they can catch and eat birds. However, there is a true spider found in southern Europe which is a real tarantula. Its body is about 2 centimetres long, and including its legs it's about 8 centimetres in all. This is a moderately poisonous spider and can give a painful bite. It doesn't spin a web and lives in a deep burrow lined with a silk-like substance. In winter it hibernates behind the silky doors it builds for its home.

This spider has been feared from Roman times. In the Middle Ages the fear got completely out of hand. (You may have noticed how some people are terrified of all spiders for no really good reason.) Anyway, a dance named the tarantella started around this time. This is done to fast music, and the legend is that it comes from the southern Italian city of Taranto. The tarantula lived in this area and apparently it was the custom to dance continually if it bit you. As long as you kept going you would be saved from death. It's not true, of course, but groups of people can be very easily affected by this kind of odd belief and have a reaction called hysteria. In Taranto they would dance for all they

were worth to survive the bite of the spider. Some must have dropped down dead from exhaustion, and so people would have believed the story even more, thinking the poison had killed them when they stopped dancing.

It is difficult to say which is the most dangerous spider in the world. I talked to one expert at London Zoo, and his choice was the Brazilian wandering spider. This has a most potent venom and a big sac to store it all in. And for another spider really worth being frightened of, you should go to Sydney, Australia. Exclusive to within 160 kilometres of the centre of Sydney lives the spider I would least like to have run up my leg. The male Sydney funnel-web spider appears to be aggressive to humans and it attacks with a bite which can kill. This is unusual for two reasons.

First, it is usually lady spiders which are dangerous. The male Australian red-back spider, for example, has such small fangs that it couldn't bite you even if it wanted to. (Unlike its deadly wife!) Second, spiders are not usually aggressive and they tend to use their venom for killing food. They only turn on us if startled. However, as I say, the Sydney funnel-web is unusual, and some books say it goes out looking for trouble. In fact this may be a little unfair on the spider because the reason why it often seems aggressive is a combination of how it and Australians conduct their social lives. The male Sydney funnel-web is very active in the breeding season. It wanders about a great deal looking for a mate. (Presumably it musn't wander further than 160 kilometres from Sydney!) Anyway, Australians lead similar outdoor social lives and this brings them and the spider into contact. So it's probably a little unfair to put all the blame for the trouble on the spider.

What poisonous spiders inject varies. The female black widow spider is only about a centimetre long, but it can give you a dose of its own very special poison. A bite from this North American "lady killer" affects certain chemicals which the body needs, and the muscles which rely on these can become paralysed.

I think one reason why the black widow is so well known is because of the part of the human body it tends to bite. It lives mainly in country areas, and often builds its web under outside-toilet seats. (It likes living in places like this because there are lots of insects to catch and eat.)

When these toilets were more common about half the bites on men were on one particular part of the body. I know of one man who was bitten (I'll just call him Willy rather than use his real name). He lived, but there were times when the pain was apparently so bad that he rather hoped he wouldn't.

The reason why this sensitive area gets "hit" by the spiders is because the black widow has poor eyesight. It has to rely on its sense of vibration. It is good at feeling things coming. When it does, WHAM! – it goes for the thing dangling closest to its jaws. It is true, though, that of the 30,000 different sorts of spider that are known in the world, most couldn't hurt you to save their lives. However, another less well-known fact is that nearly all the world's spiders are poisonous. The so-called harmless ones simply do not have strong enough jaws to break human skin. This means, for example, that the spider in the bath in the morning is almost certainly poisonous, but that you need not be frightened of it.

The really deadly spiders have very colourful names – the Australian red-back, the brown recluse of South America, the banana spider, as well as the black widow and our friend the male Sydney funnel-web – be careful, leave them all alone, and you'll be all right!

What happens when a crocodile or alligator bites you?

It's not your lucky day. However, despite what a lot of people think, crocodiles don't eat that many humans. You have to ask for trouble. They rarely climb out of the water and come looking for you.

A lot of problems come from the way people take risks with animals. They go swimming where crocodiles live. Or they tease a pet dog. One boy got eaten by a polar bear when he broke into an American zoo after it had closed for the night.

Quite a few people get eaten by the Nile crocodile in Egypt. One reason for this is that the women who do the family laundry in the river stand in the water and face the rocks on the bank. They use these rocks to beat the washing clean. The disadvantage of this style of washing is that it leaves their bottoms sticking out towards the river. They bend over backwards (or forwards I suppose you should say) to tempt the reptiles. The Nile crocodile very often gives in to this sort of temptation. About 1,000 people a year are killed by crocodiles in Africa.

Crocodile are ferocious eaters, brilliant at stalking

their prey. They quietly glide up to you with just their eyes and nostrils out of the water. There is hardly a ripple to see. When they bite you, say your head, the technique which they have developed over millions of years is to sink their teeth in, then spin their own body around. As they may be over 8 metres long and weigh more than 2 tonnes (the salt water crocodile of Asia and the Pacific is the largest reptile in the world) this rips off whatever part they have got hold of. And they carry on doing this until everything is eaten up.

As a matter of interest, the best way to tell the difference between an alligator and a crocodile is to look at the mouth. A crocodile has enlarged teeth on each side of the lower jaw. When it closes its mouth these teeth, which slant outwards, slot into a groove outside the upper jaw. They can be seen from the outside even when the beast's mouth is closed. Alligators have a different tooth arrangement and the teeth are hidden when the mouth is shut. (When I left school I went to university to study to be a dentist. For some reason I spent the first year learning all sorts of helpful facts like this, which I've never been able to forget. It may be worth knowing even if you are not going to be a dentist. If you are about to have your head bitten off by one of these reptiles at least you'll know which one is going to do it!)

Other animals bite in various ways. Much of the damage they do depends on their type of teeth. Cats have long thin sharp teeth which can stab like needles. Dogs have teeth which stretch and slash skin like a razor. Camels have hook-shaped teeth which they use for tearing leaves off desert trees. (These can give a very nasty bite, and are just one reason why you should never shave a camel!)

Of course most of us are not going to end up inside a crocodile or alligator, but cats and dogs do bite a lot of people. (There are nearly a million dog bites every year in America.) I have seen one girl whose nose was completely bitten off by a dog which someone thought was very friendly. You cannot assume that someone else's pet will let you rush up to it like your own would. It may be startled or nervous, and then turn round and snap. It only takes a second to have your nose off.

And before anyone feels too superior to other animals, it has to be said that people also get bitten by other people. I once worked in a prison and saw quite a few human bites. And not because there wasn't enough food.

What happens if you are struck by lightning?

A number of things can happen to your body as a result of this huge electric shock. Lightning can carry 100 million volts. You can compare this with overhead power lines (up to 400,000 volts), the electric chair in American prisons (2,000 volts) and the supply to homes (usually 200–250 volts).

24

There are three basic ways this energy can kill you. First, much of the damage that an electric shock causes is like a crush injury. I saw a man once who had touched a high voltage power cable. His arms could hardly have been damaged more if they had been squashed by a steam roller. Second, the electricity can cause burns to the skin. It does this both directly and by setting clothes on fire. Third, there is the physical damage that comes from being hit by something which people who have survived have said is like a blow from a sledge hammer. Arms and legs can snap like dry twigs.

To understand what happens if you are electrocuted you have to know a bit about how the electricity moves through the body. Let's take the electric chair as an example. In this method of killing people the electricity is passed through the whole body as one wire is connected to the head and the other to a leg. These are shaved so that there is good contact between the body and the electricity and the person dies instantly. Remember, electricity is like a lot of things in life. It likes to take the path of least resistance. Nerves and blood vessels offer little resistance (unlike bone and fat). So the electricity tends to follow these. All cases are different, though, and it is difficult to know from the outside the path that the shock takes. If it goes through the heart and brain, as it does in the electric chair, when the whole body takes the shock, then things are very serious.

It is important to know about electricity so you can protect yourself from the household electric supply. If your skin is wet or damp, even the lower voltage (240 volts in most houses in the United Kingdom) can kill you. The skin makes a better contact with electricity so that more can go through your body and you are in a similar position to someone in the electric chair. This is why the electrics in places such as bathrooms (where you and the floor are often wet) are usually switched on and off with long cords which reduce the chance of a good contact and someone being killed.

In case this is all a bit gruesome, here's a funny story about the electric chair. (There aren't many!) It shows what can happen if you don't think ahead. On 6 August 1890 the electric chair was used for the first time in Auburn Prison, New York. The then emperor of Abyssinia (now Ethiopia) Menelik II thought that this new device was just what his poor country needed to bring it right up to date. So he ordered three from the American firm who made them. These were packed up and duly arrived in Abyssinia. It was only after they had arrived and he unpacked his nice new electric chairs that Emperor Menelik II realised that Abyssinia had no electricity. He had nowhere to plug them in! He ended up using one as a throne.

But back to what lightning does to you. Often the immediate problem is that the heart and lungs stop working. They can sometimes be restarted, and as I said elsewhere in this book you can learn to do this fairly easily at a first aid class. The body of someone who has been struck by lightning may look very odd indeed. Apart from skin marks which have a strange leaf pattern, the clothes may be torn or burnt and the bones broken. This sometimes makes the death look suspicious. The doctors who examine the body later to try and find out what has happened have to act like detectives. Is this a freak accident or a case of murder?

In one incident a soldier was found dead near his wrecked motor bike on some lonely moorland. After a careful check it became clear no one else was involved. From the marks on the body it was seen

26

that the bolt of lightning had hit his crash helmet and that was what had caused the damage to him and to the bike.

So what can you do to avoid being struck by lightning? It has been worked out that there are 44,000 thunderstorms a day on our earth. This makes for 100 flashes of lightning every second. Some people believe very strongly in fate, and that when your time to die comes there is nothing you can do about it; they would see lightning as the hand of fate. One man in London hurrying to get out of a thunderstorm put his house key in the door lock just as the chimney was struck by lightning. The electricity came down the warm chimney and jumped across to an iron bed in the front room. From the bed it jumped across to the door lock. The shock stopped his breathing and he died. It seems very hard to plan against this sort of accident!

However, there are some general rules. If you are outdoors, get into a building or even a car, because this will help shield you from the electricity. Avoid trees (especially ones stuck out on their own) as they may guide the electricity to you. Don't stay in a group with other people, and keep moving, otherwise the body warmth rises and this tends to draw the lightning to you. I know of a group of cricketers who were struck (and one was killed) because their warmth attracted a bolt of lightning. Indoors it is best to keep away from the chimney where hot air – as in the house of the man putting the key in the lock – can guide the electricity down to you.

Anyway, all this is interesting, but to be hit by lightning is very rare. Far more important to worry about is the electricity around all of us: in the wires that carry electricity for light and heating in schools and houses; in the cables to garden mowers and hedge trimmers; and in the high power lines of electric trains. If you're careful near these you can avoid accidents. (About 1,000 people every year are killed in electrical accidents in the USA, and in the United Kingdom about 30 people a year die in their own homes by being electrocuted.) So beware when playing near electric cables (they nearly always have signs up to warn you they're there). In the home, do not play with electric sockets. You are asking for trouble if you stick a fork in a plug point.

The classic case of playing about with electricity was the famous experiment of the American scientist and statesman Benjamin Franklin in 1752. He flew a silk kite during a thunderstorm to prove what lightning really was. The kite attracted the electricity from the clouds and conducted it down to the earth along the wet string. He tied a metal key on the end of the string and made a spark between this key and the earth. He must have been very brave if he really understood what was happening. As it happened the current missed him, but this sort of experiment is

extremely dangerous. Do not try it yourself. A
Russian scientist called Richmann repeated the experiment in 1753 using an iron rod and was killed.

But to end on a happy note, you can only really
know what it is like to be struck by lightning if it happens to you. Two patients of mine were on honey-
moon in a small tent. Night had fallen and they had
cuddled up together on a mountain side when lightning struck their tent pole. They were both unhurt
and wondered at first what had happened. I asked
them later what it was like to be hit by 100 million
volts. They said they hadn't really been bothered.
There was a flash and a tingle, but it was their first
night of marriage and they thought love was always
going to be like this!

*If you were burnt all over, would you be all right if
you were quickly covered in butter?*

No. It is not a good idea to put butter on a burn.
I think it is supposed to help stop the pain by
keeping the air away. (This was what my Mum
thought, anyway, until I put her straight!) However,
touching the burn by putting anything like butter on
it, and especially by pricking any blisters, can cause a
dangerous infection.

A burn may go right through the skin, or just damage the outer layer. Surprisingly enough the deep
burn may not be painful, because all the nerves are
gone. This is often a very merciful thing. Most of us
have had the more painful and less serious burns,
such as you get from touching a hot cooker.

It is important to try and relieve any pain, and to

get someone badly burnt to hospital fast, as well as trying to keep the wound clean. However, the sad fact is that anyone burnt all over is likely to die. In fact anyone with more than half (50 per cent) of their body burnt is probably going the same way.

You can work out how much of someone is burnt by using the flat of the hand as a guide. This is about 1 per cent of your total body area. So if you burnt an area equivalent to ten hands, then you would have burnt 10 per cent of your body surface area. (A leg is about 18 per cent, an arm 9 per cent.)

The more you are burnt, the more serious things are. The reason for this is partly infection again, but mainly because, with so much skin destroyed, body fluids leak out as fast, if not faster, than they can be replaced. I can remember one terrible case where a young girl was burnt when a car petrol tank exploded and caught fire. All her skin was burnt off. We had fairly limited medical aid in this remote area of the world, and, although we knew she would probably die, we kept her alive for some days until her family could fly her back to Europe. (She died peacefully in a special burns unit at home.)

The point of this sad story is that it shows how dangerous fire can be – and how fast any kind of accident with it can happen. This particular fire destroyed her in seconds.

It's important to realise that burns can come in many forms – sunburn, friction burns (the sort of thing that happens when you slide down a rope), chemical burns from substances such as acid or caustic soda, and burns from electric shocks. So whether you are standing too close to an open fire in a nightdress, sunning yourself on a desert island, mixing chemicals in a science lesson or going for a walk during a thunderstorm – BEWARE!

What happens if you have a fever and you are in the desert?

Having a high temperature when you are ill with something like a bad throat or a sore ear is a complicated business. One reason that the temperature rises is because the germs put it up. Being in the desert would make it a lot harder for you to cool off. The practical question is whether you should try and bring the high temperature down, or whether you should stay hot and "sweat it out" – after all, my Granny used to tell me to wrap up warm when I was feverish.

Lizards certainly like heat when they feel ill. They are cold blooded, which means their body temperature is the same as the air temperature where they are. When they're sick they crawl off and lie in the sun. If they cannot do this, they take much longer to get better. The obvious conclusion is that having a

high temperature actually helps them fight the infection.

But most doctors nowadays would disagree with my Granny over keeping people hot when they have a fever. Humans are warm blooded, unlike lizards, and their temperature should stay more or less at 37°C – in the desert or not. High temperatures can bring on fits or convulsions, particularly if you're under five. So when you're ill you shouldn't overdo blankets, warm fire and hot-water bottles. The right medicine, iced drinks and a cool flannel are much more important for getting you better.

It's usually only when you're ill that you need so much help in staying at the correct temperature. When you are well the human body has a number of clever ways of keeping you around 37°C wherever you are (though it varies a bit during the day and is lowest when you are asleep). When it is hot – like in the desert – you need to lose heat. The body sweats and as this sweat goes into the air, heat goes with it. (Dogs can't sweat. You will see them panting instead on a hot day.) Also the skin increases the amount of blood flowing through it. It does this by widening its blood vessels. This brings quite a lot of blood close to the body surface, where it loses heat rather like a radiator. The skin of a grown-up weighs nearly 3 kilograms. So it's quite a large part of the body and you can lose a lot of heat through it.

In hot parts of the world this control of the body temperature can go wrong. Heat stroke is a condition where the temperature of the body rises to above 40°C. This can kill a previously fit person. (The highest anyone has survived at is 46·5°C.) Anyone found suffering with it needs to be cooled quickly. When my Dad was at sea during the Second World War they had a man on board with heat stroke. This is often a problem when soldiers train hard in hot weather wearing full uniform, especially if they have come from colder climates (my Dad was sailing from England to South Africa.) The others on the ship helped save his life by hosing him down with cold water.

Two particularly tricky places to "stay cool" on a ship are the engine room and the galley (kitchen to any landlubbers.) On one expedition I was on, we sailed in only two weeks from the ice of the Antarctic to the Equator. It became incredibly hot below decks. It was especially bad near the engines and ovens. I gave the men who had to work there extra salt to take for a few days because a lot is lost in sweat. If salt and water are not replaced you can get what is called heat exhaustion. It's not usually necessary to take extra salt for long. When you get used to the heat you can take quite enough in your food.

You might think that being warm blooded is more trouble than it's worth. You could argue that it's far better to be a cold blooded reptile like our lizard friend, simply going along with the temperature round about.

The problem with this is that it restricts where you can live. Most reptiles live in hot parts of the world. Few can survive in the colder parts of Europe or America. When they do live in cold places they have to hibernate all winter. Not a brilliant idea for us – we spend a third of our lives asleep already.

How long could you last at the South Pole if you had no clothes on?

Not long. The Antarctic gets down to below −55°C at times. This can be compared to the temperature in a freezer. The one in my kitchen as I write this is storing ice cream very nicely at only −20°C. Just as the body can keep itself cool by actions such as sweating when things heat up, so it can try and keep warm when things cool off. Blood moves away from the skin (so you look paler) and deep into the warm centre of the body where it won't be lost so easily. As well as this diversion of blood, the muscles can shiver. This trembling, shaking action burns up body fuel. This makes heat just as burning coal does. However, there's no way this could keep you at 37°C in the Antarctic if you had nothing on. You need to wear the right clothes – something with a little more protection than your birthday suit. When I was down near the South Pole we wore layers of clothes to trap air around the body. This kept me warm in the same way as a duvet does in bed. I also had a special jacket with flaps to keep the wind out of places such as the sleeves. Snow, rain and the wind soon chill you. Rain on the skin cools you like sweat does. That's why you feel extra cold when you get wet.

You don't have to go to the South Pole to die of cold. Bad European winters kill many old people. There are a number of reasons why. The elderly may not be active and able to move around and make their own heat as younger people can. They may be too poor to buy fuel for heating. Also, the body has a mechanism for picking up that it's getting cold, when actions like shivering can start. In some old

people this personal thermostat fails to work and they can develop what is called hypothermia. It's as if a house temperature has fallen and the central heating hasn't switched on.

One unusual problem in cold parts of the world is frostbite. This is a burn caused by severe cold, when areas of the skin or whole fingers, toes and noses turn black and die. Another thing to be careful of is that something made of metal takes heat away from the body so quickly that if you touch it when it is very cold, the skin will stick. Water in the skin freezes and acts as a sort of Superglue. If you take photographs in places such as Antarctica you must be very careful of putting a metal camera to your face.

I have heard of this sort of thing happening in

Europe, too. Cars left out in the cold overnight can have frozen door locks in the morning. One man in a hurry to get to work put his lips to the lock to try and melt the ice. He ended up stuck in a surprise "kiss" with his car.

So beware of the cold. Remember that old people may need help in the winter. And don't take your clothes off at the South Pole.

What could you do if the only food left in the world was slugs?

Get to like them. Those of us who are lucky enough to live in a part of the world where there is lots of food can pick and choose. Millions of people are not so lucky.

I have never eaten slugs, but I have had snails and I'd guess they're much the same – rather tasteless unless cooked with something like garlic butter to give some flavour.

I've never had to eat rats but fried mouse tastes like chicken. I know this from people who ate it to try and protect themselves from whooping cough. It wasn't until the 1940s that whooping cough vaccination began to be widely used, so there are still a lot of people around who can remember the days before this when families only had folklore remedies to fight this terrible disease.

I'm not suggesting we all rush out to eat rat, but you're missing a lot if you turn your nose up at other people's food. I know English people who go off on foreign travels and ignore local food. They like to sit swilling beer, and stuffing down the fish and chips they can eat every day at home.

Most sensible travellers get to enjoy local dishes. The best food I've ever had was a dish of octopus curry cooked with prawns from Madagascar. I also used to like curried Indian Ocean fruit bats, but I've stopped eating them now to save them from being shot.

Locusts, ants cooked in butter, and moth larvae are all highly prized by wealthy people in places such as Africa and Thailand. And for the poor, too, "unusual" foods can be very important. The Isoko tribe in Nigeria get a great deal of the protein they need from rats, snails, mud-fish and palm-weevils. They also have to eat frogs. These frogs are the same animals that the rich swallow down with fine wines in the best Parisian restaurants. The only difference is that the people in Paris are not eating them to stay alive.

You must still think before you eat. It is an interesting fact that the most active poison known to man comes from a species of South American frog. Local Indians extract it from the frogs to tip their arrows when hunting other animals. However, the frog itself has not got a poisonous bite. The poison is in its skin. So you would have to bite the frog. There's no worry about the frog biting you!

What's it like to drown?

You may be surprised to know that there are quite a few people around who can tell you. I have a friend who certainly can. People who have come very close to death – or have "died" and been saved by first aid – tell different stories. Some see their whole life flash before them. My friend simply felt that she was floating and falling asleep. Many tell of trying desperately to hold their breath – which isn't a surprising thing to want to do – and a feeling of panic at being under water and unable to breathe. Water may be swallowed. In some cases I have had to examine, there has been water in the stomach after death.

Drowning usually ends in death after water gets into the lungs. This can be called "wet drowning". A person can also die without water even getting into the lungs. This is sometimes called "dry drowning". The shock of going into water – often if it is very cold – can cause the muscles in the wall of the main airway to tighten, and this will narrow the entrance to the lungs. Although water doesn't get down into the lungs, the oxygen is still cut off and the victim very quickly loses consciousness. Sometimes the shock also stops the heart. The reason why you may be taught to splash water on to the back of your neck before the first plunge into a swimming pool is to make this less of a shock.

"Dry drowning" is quite common. This is what is thought to have happened in the "brides in the bath" murders. This famous case came to trial in 1915. A man called George Smith murdered at least three young women for money in the same unusual way. When they were in the bath he would lift their knees and, as they slipped down, push their heads under and hold them there. It is thought that the sudden shock of this narrowed their upper airways and killed them.

Smith said the women had died accidentally. However, in court he was unlucky enough to come up against a famous doctor called Sir Bernard Spilsbury. Spilsbury was one of the first real medical detectives, and made it his job to find out why people died. He worked out exactly how Smith must have done the deed.

First he proved that the baths used were so small it was impossible to drown accidentally. (Smith bought a zinc tub especially for the first murder. He got half-a-crown off because it had no taps!) Then Spilsbury and a Detective Neil used a nurse in a bathing costume to show the court exactly how they thought Smith had killed the women. In fact they put on such a good display that they nearly killed the nurse. She had to be revived before the trial could continue.

There was a lot to interest people in the case. Smith – who apparently hardly ever took baths himself – was fascinating to women. He was also pretty good on the harmonium, which is a keyboard instrument like an organ. After one of his murders a witness heard him playing the hymn "Nearer my God to Thee". He was found guilty and hanged at Maidstone Prison on Friday 13 August 1915. An unlucky Friday for him, anyway.

Back to wet drowning, there are two gases involved when we breathe – oxygen and carbon dioxide. We take in oxygen, which is what we all need to stay alive. As it is used up, the carbon dioxide level in the body rises and often the victim simply cannot resist gasping for breath. (This instinct to take breaths is why you cannot kill yourself by holding your breath.) Or, in trying not to gasp, the person may become unconscious and then start to breathe. Either way, the water goes down into the lungs. There is oxygen in it, of course, but unless you have gills like fish have you can't get at it.

It is important to know that it's really the build-up of carbon dioxide, and not the fall in oxygen, that makes you want to breathe. If you go snorkelling and take a lot of deep breaths before you dive under, you run the risk of getting rid of too much carbon dioxide, and then there may not be enough to warn your brain to come up for oxygen. This has caused a lot of snorkellers to drown. So only take one deep breath before you go under.

The next stage of drowning, when the water has entered the lungs, is very interesting. It isn't simply a matter of not being able to breathe air. The events depend on whether you are drowning in fresh water or sea water. Not a lot of people realise the difference. To them drowning is drowning. But this is not always the case.

When fresh water gets into the lungs it moves quickly from there into the blood. This obviously makes the blood more watery. There are millions of red blood cells floating about in the circulation and, although they can change shape and squeeze into small blood vessels, they cannot stretch to take in so much extra water. The change in blood puts a strain on their walls and they burst like pricked balloons. This releases a substance called potassium, which can flood out and stop the heart.

In salt water, death from drowning can take four or five times longer. This is because the salt holds the water in the lungs. In fact even more can be drawn in from the blood. So the lungs become soggy, and the

40

person dies slowly as the heart fails under the strain of this.

So drowning can be either a quick or slow death depending on lots of things, including what sort of water you drown in. From accounts of survivors, it isn't always particularly unpleasant, although many people are frightened of it – just as many are frightened of being burnt in a fire. When I was in the Antarctic in 1979 our ship was caught in a terrible storm. This lasted two days and with the huge waves tossing the ship around and gale-force winds blowing icebergs at us I really thought that I had had it. There was nothing I could do and we were 3,000 kilometres from any help. So I began to work out an alternative death to drowning. I was terrified of going into the water and suffocating. However, I soon realised that the extreme cold of the water would kill me in seconds – far faster than any poison I could find – and this cheered me up a great deal as I was thrown around my cabin, praying for the storm to end.

My friend Karen Spencer fell into warm fresh water. She was on a school river-boat trip, sitting on the edge of a cruiser when another boat hit it. This bump knocked her into the water. Her mistake was not to be wearing a life jacket. Then her hair caught in the boat's propeller, and no one could get her out. It's always hard to know how long something like this goes on, because time seems to speed up or stand still in these sorts of emergencies, but she was held under water in the river for at least ten minutes. When she was cut free and brought out on to the bank she was really "dead". All her school friends looked away, because they couldn't bear to see her body cold, blue and wet. However, there was one man in the crowd who had done some first aid. He

41

set to work and revived her. I first met Karen in hospital when she was recovering from literally coming back from the dead.

The reason that this can happen is a bit complicated. Part of it seems to be because we have kept an ability of some distant relatives from the animal kingdom. Remember that dolphins, whales, and porpoises are mammals like us, not fish. And they can dive underwater and stay down for long periods. They do this by careful use of what oxygen is available. Only essential areas of the body get oxygen. Top of this list to be supplied is the brain.

We seem to have inherited some of this reflex from ancestors we have in common with dolphins. This is one way we can survive drowning. Also if the drowning is in cold water this can help survival by putting the body into a kind of hibernation. Young children especially should never be given up for dead after seeming to drown. They have been saved long after they have seemed to be dead.

Karen was lucky that someone had tried to revive her. We never found out who the man on the bank was. He slipped back into the crowd when the ambulance arrived.

If you find someone who you think has drowned then the vital things to do are to get air into the lungs in place of water, and to get the heart going if it has stopped. The basic technique which you should learn is called artificial resuscitation. (It's actually easier to do than to spell!) The best place to learn this is at a first aid course. However the basics are these. Clear the mouth and airways of anything like vomit, seaweed and false teeth. Then breathe for the patient, blowing air into the lungs – this is called the "kiss of life". If the heart has stopped, it needs to be massaged through the chest. You literally make it "beat" and pump blood (into which you have got some oxygen with the kiss of life) until either help arrives or the heart starts again on its own.

It is a rather strange fact that so many people drown when the human body does actually float in water. Air in the lungs acts like a life jacket. However, unless the water is very salty – as it is in the Dead Sea where you can float high enough to read a newspaper – it can be difficult to be in a position to breathe. Obviously you must have either the nose or the mouth out of the water.

There is an art to "floating" so you can breathe. Even if you cannot swim it's worth learning. Why not practise in your local swimming pool? If everyone could float and not panic there would be a lot fewer deaths from drowning.

What happens if you fall into shark-infested water?

You might get eaten alive. I've seen a man live who had his leg eaten below the knee. On the other hand the sharks may ignore you. No one really knows why some sharks attack humans and some don't, or why they may single out one particular person. In 1952 a Californian shark ate a 17-year-old boy, and ignored the five men in the water trying to save him.

Blood in the water seems to give them an appetite. I was sailing in shark-infested seas once, and I got the chance to do some fishing. I mixed up some kitchen waste, and added a few syringefuls of human blood, which my ship mates had kindly donated. I put all this in a plastic bin liner and dangled it over the side on a thick rope. There didn't seem to be any fish about so I went down below to get my rod and the bait. (Our cook had given me some steaks from the fridge!) When I got back the bag had been ripped to pieces and there were huge sharks everywhere. I caught one, but the captain later stopped me attracting them, in case anyone working on the ship fell in.

From what I have seen of sharks they do deserve their reputation, although it has to be said that actual attacks are not common. Places like Australia and South Africa seem to be the worst for man-eaters. However, I know a man who has been bitten where the local sharks were supposed to be friendly. Not only that but, as he paddled frantically back to the beach on his sail board, the shark followed him, trying to get another mouthful. We were never certain what type of shark it was. It seems most likely to have been a mako. This close relative of the great white shark is a man-eater and lives in deep water –

it was very deep close to the reef where we were. It also leaps out of the water when hooked on a rod and line – apparently this shark came out of the water to get at his leg.

One theory why my friend might have been bitten is that the shark simply bumped into him when he fell off his board. Or it may have been that the first bite was as he trailed his tasty-looking leg in the water. Some of the attacks on Californian surf boarders have been explained because the great white shark feeds on sea lions. If you are on a surf board there is a chance that from below a shark could mistake you for one of these. However, that theory does not always apply. There were no sea lions in the part of the world where my friend appeared on the shark's menu. It's clear no one can really be certain what goes on inside a shark's head.

One of the most remarkable true stories I have ever come across concerns a large Australian tiger shark. The story began on 28 April 1935 when the shark was caught alive in Sydney harbour and put in an aquarium. Soon after this it vomited and brought up a man's arm. This arm had a tattoo of two boxers on it – with this and the fingerprints on the hand as clues, the police found out who the man was. The arm appeared to have been cut off with a sharp knife. It also seemed to have the marks of gunshots. (All this gave the shark a rather good alibi.) The police arrested two men but no one found out for certain what had happened.

One theory was that the man, who was a 40-year-old ex-boxer called James Smith, was killed, cut up, and dumped at sea in a trunk. Either there was no room in the trunk for the arm or it somehow came out. Then the tiger shark ate the limb, but it was caught before it could digest its meal!

What this does show is that sharks are not that fussy. They'll eat you dead or alive. (Everything from car number plates to a bulldog still on its lead have been found inside them.)

A lot of attacks happen when fishermen are catching other fish. If a wounded fish is wriggling on your speargun and there is blood in the water it seems to me that you're asking for trouble. I can remember fishing over a reef in the Indian Ocean. Again the local sharks were supposed to be small and friendly, and I'd actually been swimming with them. The friend I was with decided to go for a large fish which had been pinching our bait and breaking our line all day. While he baited up a stronger rod I cleaned away the blood from our day's catch and washed the fish over the side of our small dinghy. It was getting dark when he hooked this mysterious fish. I was taking pictures for a fishing magazine so I stopped gutting our catch and got my camera ready.

At last a large reef fish called a grouper broke the surface. As it came towards the boat a 3-metre shark suddenly appeared behind it and bit clean through the body leaving my friend holding just the fish's head, still on the hook. I have got some great pictures of this. In one it is difficult to see which looks more shocked – the grouper's head or my friend. Presumably the shark had been attracted by the fish blood in the water. However, I'm sure it would have had my hands given the chance. I never swam over this reef again.

So be very careful if anyone warns you about sharks. Don't do anything to make yourself an attractive meal like I did with the blood all over my hands. And if there are shark nets up, swim in the places you are told to.

There are lots of other dangerous fish in the sea. Many experts agree that the stone fish is the most poisonous. To those that don't, all I can say is that they have never seen somebody who has stood on one! The stone fish has grooved spines along its back. Each of these is attached to a couple of poison sacs. The fish itself looks like a brown lump of coral – difficult to see, but very easy to feel. A fisherman friend of mine from the Seychelles trod on a big one and said the pain was so bad he wanted to die. He lay on his iron bed and gripped the frame so hard that when he looked at it later it was twisted out of shape. No normal person could ever have bent it. The agony gave him the strength of ten men.

After this he used the local traditional cure for the poisoning – that is to "boil" your foot. Actually the water temperature should be just bearable. The poison is a protein. Proteins are natural substances that make up much of our bodies, for example our muscles, and there are very many of them. However, some proteins – like the poison of the stone fish – are damaging and painful if they are injected into the body. So the theory is that if you "cook" this protein,

it will lose its strength rather in the way that cooked meat becomes tender. My friend overdid his foot and ended up with one looking like an elephant's. (This is not something that you should ever try yourself.) The pain of treading on a stone fish really is the most dreadful feeling. A man from the other side of the island died of it. Morphine is one of the strongest painkillers a doctor will ever use. However, even an injection of this will not always relieve the pain.

After stings from some fish it may be possible to numb the nerve that runs to where you've been injured. I know a traveller who stood on a sting-ray while scuba diving off Sri Lanka. When various tablets failed to work, a doctor injected a painkiller around a nerve at the ankle, which blocked off the pain. However, this does need special equipment and of course not everybody travels with a doctor.

The sea has some strange and frightening creatures. By the way, so have rivers. A bus drove into a

South American river in 1976 and 31 people were eaten alive by the dreaded piranha fishes. And there is a puffer fish in Asia which is apparently attracted to urine. It so likes the smell of it in the water that it will "attack" and bite your private parts if you pass water while swimming near it. A small South American catfish has similar tastes. It may even try to wriggle inside you to get at the urine! I have never seen this in my travels, but you'll never catch me swimming without my trunks.

What would happen if you went over Niagara Falls in a barrel?

You might well be killed. People have done it and lived. But then one man called Brian Latasa touched a 230,000 volt power line in California in November 1967 and came through. That doesn't mean that touching electricity is safe. There's always someone – often with a loud voice – who will tell you about what he or she has or hasn't done, such as smoked cigarettes for 50 years, or drunk whisky all day. The problem is that you don't hear from the people who haven't survived. The churchyard is full of them.

Although you may not ever go over Niagara Falls in a barrel there is a similar situation closer to home: being in a car crash. If you are in a car (or a barrel) and it hits something, you are likely to get hurt. Much of the damage is because your body is thrown about. The people who have lived after their drop in the barrel have usually wedged themselves in. You can't do this in a car. So, whether you are in the front or back seat, it is best to wear seat belts if the car has them. Even if a car crashes as you're driving quietly through a town, for a passenger it is like being dropped on to concrete from a third storey window. And young people are lighter than grown-ups, which means they are thrown about more easily. They are turned into high velocity missiles when cars crash. Grown-ups would never carry eggs loose on the back seat of their car. Ask them if they would, if they intend to carry you "loose" and do not strap you in with a seat belt.

I have been in several car accidents. The worst one was in America when I was a medical student. Four of us were travelling around in a camper van seeing the country. One night we were driving across the plains of South Dakota on a straight motorway that was built up high above the corn fields. I was in the front talking to the driver. (It was my job to keep her awake.) My two other friends were asleep in the back. After a while I suddenly realised that the driver had fallen asleep too.

The camper van simply drove straight off the edge of the road before I could do anything. I wasn't wearing a seat belt and it was a bit like being a marble in a tin can that's being kicked down the road. One minute we all hit the roof. The next moment I was bounced half out of the window. I counted hitting the floor at least four times before we ground to a halt.

You may think that bandits, sharks and shipwrecks are the big killers on expeditions. In fact, whether you are at home, being driven to school, or on an adventure, it makes no difference: one of the biggest killers of children and grown-ups under about forty is road traffic accidents. I was lucky. Only our dog was actually killed in my accident. But I have worn a seat belt ever since.

The other lesson I learnt was to try and think clearly in such situations. I was the first to recover from the shock of the crash and I pulled a girl out of the back of the camper through a broken window. She wasn't actually injured until I cut her bottom on the glass doing this. It's easy to make these sorts of mistakes in the heat of the moment. (I thought the van might catch fire – that was my excuse, anyway.)

I know one first aider who bravely crawled under a crashed car to help a trapped driver. He carefully bandaged the man's broken leg. The problems came when the ambulance men arrived and tried to get the man out. Our friend had accidentally bandaged the leg to the car's exhaust pipe. This had to be cut off by the fire brigade before they could get the driver out, and he went to hospital with the exhaust still strapped to his leg.

GRRRRR

What's it like to be stung by the most painful thing in the world?

It is awful. I must tell you a little story. When I had nearly finished this book I went off to have a holiday on a tropical desert island out in the Indian Ocean. I planned to fish and think about things. (For one thing this book still did not have a title.)

The first day there I could hardly wait to get out. I waded out chest deep into the tropical sea with my rod and began to cast my line and catch fish. I was doing very well. It was so hectic that I had to keep the bait down my swimming trunks. There was no time to keep wading back from the coral reef to my tackle box on the beach. Life was wonderful.

I began to think about this book. There is an expression grown-ups use – "do as I say, not as I do" – and I was thinking about this and what I'd written about sharks when I looked down in the water. Blood from my fresh fish bait was drifting out into the current from my swimming trunks. A few feet away a large shark was cruising about. I shot back to the beach. (You have to remember that this was the island where I knew sharks ate people!) Getting my breath back, I sat thinking about my narrow escape from the shark, and then about all the stone fish there must have been around my bare feet. I should have learnt a lesson from all this (at first I thought I would keep quiet and not mention it in this book) but by that evening I was walking along the beach without a care in the world. Accidents only happened to other people. I had got away with being careless. The world was a fine place.

I suddenly had the worst pain I've ever had in my life. First my foot felt as if a lighted cigarette had been stubbed out on it. Then dreadful electric shocks began shooting up my leg. My body felt as if it was on fire and sweat started to pour off me. I could not believe the pain. My first worry was I would collapse before I could get help. I would die before I could even tell anyone what had happened.

Anyway, to cut the story short, I lived (you had worked that out!) but I couldn't use my foot – I had been walking barefooted on the beach and had been stung by one of the scorpions that lived there in sandy burrows. It was some weeks before I walked properly again.

There are lots of things in life which people are scared of. A survey in the USA of 3,000 people showed that speaking in public was first on the list, and fear of heights was second. Insects and bugs such as the scorpion were third. It seems that scorpions should perhaps be higher on the list, following some research done in Trinidad to see what happened to people they stung. (Trinidad can be a particularly bad place for these stings because the Trinidad black scorpion, which is a very nasty piece of work, lives in the sugar cane and cocoa plantations, and stings people who work there.) Most of the grown-ups were all right apart from the pain. (Only one out of 400 died.) However, when scorpions stung children under five a quarter of those children died.

The important thing to learn from my own painful story, which I decided in the end I had to own up to, is that you have to look after yourself in life. Books, grown-ups, and various other people like police and doctors can help you some of the time. But finally you have to look after yourself.

How do you know when someone is dead?

You find out if the person's heart has stopped beating. This isn't always as easy as it sounds. It's all very well if you are in a bright new hospital with all the latest equipment. But people die in other places, and often in the most difficult conditions, such as in fires and car crashes. There is all the difference in the world between a hospital bed and a wet ditch on a rainy night. It's not so easy then, I can tell you. Try listening for a faint heart beat in a light aircraft during a tropical storm. I had to once, and it was impossible to know what had really happened until we landed.

When I was about eight a fat lady fainted at a local church fête. No one knew what to do. Grown-ups were running about like frightened chickens. Someone took the fat lady's false teeth out and laid them on the ground. This wasn't a bad idea at all. She could have choked on them. However, someone then trod on them.

A man tried to give her a drink of water. (Never give an unconscious person something to drink. This could be choked on, too.) Then the vicar produced a mirror from his wife's handbag and held it under the fat lady's nose. This got us nowhere. Other people were shouting things to do and doing nothing. Finally the lady got up and dusted herself down and was looking for her teeth just as the local doctor arrived. (I'd finally been sent to get him.)

What should have been done was to check whether her heart was beating. You do this by feeling for a pulse. This is the "thump" you can feel in an artery's wall as the heart pushes out blood.

Forget about holding a mirror under the nose. The

54

idea of this is that if the person is breathing you'll see the breath on the glass. It's not reliable, and we don't all carry mirrors. You only need a breeze to blow the breath away, and someone who has only fainted is on the way to the undertaker's.

So how do you find a place on the body where you can feel a pulse? In films they always seem to get down on one knee, hold the patient's limp wrist, and look at a watch. (Groucho Marx used to joke, "Either this man is dead or my watch has stopped!")

This pulse at the wrist isn't always easy to feel. Try it on yourself. Put one hand flat down on a table with the palm uppermost. Use the fingertips of the other hand to feel on the part of the wrist facing up, a couple of centimetres from where the hand joins the arm. With some practice and luck you should get quite good at finding the beat of the heart. (This should be the side with the thumb on if you've done it properly.)

However, it is not that easy to do in an emergency; and some quite normal people do not have this pulse to feel. So what do you do if you are at a fête and a fat lady collapses?

Go for the neck! There is always a pulse there if the heart is beating, and the high pressure is easy to feel because the artery is as thick as a finger and just under the skin. When Sir Walter Raleigh had his head cut off in 1618 by two blows of the executioner's axe, those watching commented on how the blood gushed out of his neck, even though he was an old man.

If you want to practise feeling for one of your own arteries in your neck, use your fingertips and feel gently just to one side of the Adam's apple.

There is another good place to feel: in the groin there's a big artery running close to the skin as it travels down to the leg. Doctors feel for this one a lot.

However, many of their patients are lying in bed
with very few clothes on. You have to be practical
when it comes to first aid. It's not always on to go
putting your hand up a lady's dress at a fête, and it
can be very difficult to get your hands round tight

corsets, so I would stick to feeling the neck. If there isn't a pulse there, it's likely that the heart has stopped. This is called a cardiac arrest. You may be able to start it again – you'll need to learn how at a first aid class. Why not find out where there is one near you and see if you can join?

Experts spend a lot of time talking about the exact moment someone "dies". They usually agree that it's actually when the brain dies. As this will happen straight after the heart stops sending blood to the brain, you can consider that if the heart stops someone is dead.

Other conditions can be confused with death, such as faints and being knocked out. In fact there are lots of reasons why someone may seem dead. Extreme cold, for example, can make a body appear very dead indeed. Even doctors get caught out from time to time. There are cases every now and again in the newspapers where a doctor has said that someone is dead who isn't. This must give the people who are about to arrange the funeral a very pleasant surprise.

I had a group of friends who were miles from anywhere in the middle of the Atlantic Ocean on a ship. One of them collapsed while he was working in the engine room. After four hours of trying to bring him round, the others couldn't decide if he was dead or not. (He was in fact.) One of the crew had worked in a place where they keep dead people before burial, so the captain sent for him, and asked what he thought. This man said all the dead people he had seen had blue feet. So they looked at the feet, and as they were blue the man was pronounced dead.

I'm not making fun of this. All these men were my friends. When I joined the ship later they were still very upset at losing a ship mate, even though they had done everything possible to save him. However,

I know many people with blue feet who have years to live. They would be very unhappy if you said they were dead.

So it can be very difficult to know when a person is dead. But it's very important to know how to find out, and to be able to try and revive the person. One day it may literally be the difference between life and death for someone you know.

Can you choke by running with a gobstopper in your mouth?

Yes. Sweets can easily slip back and block off the airways when you are running and breathing quickly. Especially if you get an unexpected knock. Then they can become "lungstoppers". It doesn't just happen with sweets. I know of one man who put the white ball from a pool table in his mouth for a bet. Then he couldn't get it out and he choked to death. The fact that choking can kill is why grown-ups worry so much when they see children running around with toys and sweets in their mouths. It is best not to do it.

One of the basic rules about first aid is that you must keep the air passages open to prevent choking. People who are unconscious must be laid out on the ground on their sides, not on their backs. If a casualty lies like this, face down, the tongue and anything else that could get in the way (vomit, false teeth, or seaweed if you have pulled someone out of the sea) will fall forwards, or out of the mouth, rather than back down the throat. If anything does go back and block off the airways, the person runs out of oxygen and dies. The body can't last long without oxygen. (One man did stay underwater in a swimming pool for 13 minutes once without breathing, but this is quite exceptional.)

There are other emergencies to do with getting air in and out of the lungs. For example with asthma the airways are narrowed, and breathing is difficult and wheezy. The sufferer often says the chest seems "tight". This is something that can be helped with the right medical treatment.

There is a worm somewhere in the world which breathes through its bottom! Quite what would happen if it choked or got asthma is hard to imagine.

What happens if you are hit by a cannon ball?

You are going to get hurt. A typical cannon ball weighs about 4–5 kilograms. Just one of these could easily kill a dozen men if they were standing in line.

In the old days much would depend on where and how it hit you. At sea, even if the ball itself actually missed your body, it could still splinter the wooden side of the ship and send oak daggers flying into you. On land things would be a little different. The Battle of Waterloo took place in June 1815. Luckily 18 June was a wet day and the soft ground saved much injury because the cannon balls did not bounce around.

All sorts of other weapons – swords, lances, bayonets and pikes – also caused dreadful wounds during the battle. These days the weapons may have changed, but the wounds and their dangers have not.

Bleeding is usually the first sign of injury. And the first person to give aid has to try and stop this quickly. There are about 6 litres of blood in a grown-up and when a large artery or vein is cut open it doesn't take long for it to come out. First let's take a look at the most dramatic sort of bleeding.

A butcher carving meat off the bone of a carcase that's hanging up should cut upwards. The reason for this is that if a knife slips suddenly when you are cutting down (it's actually much easier to hold the knife like a dagger and cut down), it's in a perfect position to stab you in the groin. Try it without anything in your hand and see. Make a fist above your head, and swing the straight arm down as a careless butcher might. Your fist will hit your body exactly where the knife would cut you.

Unfortunately this area at the top of the leg is exactly the spot where big blood vessels lie unprotected just under the skin. They are carrying all the blood to the leg. If an artery is cut here you have probably only about a minute in which to save the wounded person's life. With this sort of accident, even if you are only young, your effort in time may be better than expert help too late. Do not wander off to phone for a doctor or to get a bandage. The person could be dead by the time you get back. You should lay the casualty down and put pressure on the bleeding area. Press hard enough to stop the blood coming out – a bit harder than when you are sticking a stamp on an envelope. After 5-10 minutes the bleeding will almost certainly have stopped. Otherwise keep going for up to 15 minutes – any longer than this and the person's leg could "die". This is because when you press on this area (a pressure point) you may completely cut off the leg's blood supply (rather like blocking a motorway).

It may be difficult with a leg, but if possible raise any cut area. Blood is like water. It flows faster downhill than up. If you cut a hand it is fairly easy to raise it above the head; this will make it harder work for your heart to pump blood up than it would be to pump it down, and so less blood will be lost.

I hope you never do see an accident like the one with the butcher's knife. If you do, you will see the difference between cutting an artery and cutting a vein. Arteries spurt blood like an oil well that has blown its top. This is because blood is pumped through these to all parts of the body and there is a high pressure of blood. Veins ooze, as the blood is going back to the heart at a lower pressure in these. A large vein can bleed in a similar way to a water-filled balloon that has been gashed with a razor. It is very difficult to actually pinpoint where the leak is, so the bleeding can be more difficult to stop – at least you can see where arterial blood is spurting from. Things are even more difficult if you can't see what's going on at all. This can happen if you bleed internally, for example into the space around the intestines.

The result of the loss of so much blood is a condition called "shock". It is important to understand what this really means. There are four meanings of the word in my dictionary! The one I am talking about is when blood fails to get to vital parts of the body. This is what happens when there is heavy bleeding.

Shock shows itself in a number of ways. The only real way to learn how to recognise it is to see it in the flesh. As the body tries to make up for the lost blood, the heart beats faster, the skin goes pale, cold and sweaty, the breathing speeds up, and the patient looks and feels awful. Once seen a few times this condition becomes easier to spot. It is important to be able to do this because if the bleeding is hidden then the shock may be the only sign that something serious is happening.

There are special problems too when other parts of the body bleed. For example the scalp bleeds very heavily when cut, because there are a lot of blood vessels there. The trouble with putting pressure on the top of the head after an injury is that there may be a fracture underneath. It is worth learning what to do in this case and in other tricky areas – such as noses, tooth sockets and palms – at a first aid class.

Most cuts are not as serious as the butcher's groin injury. Nor will you see many wounds caused by cannon balls. But if you do get involved with first aid work you will see a whole variety of bleeding wounds: ragged tears caused by barbed wire and dog's teeth; crushes and bruises from falls and blows; and puncture wounds from stabs with needles and garden forks (these often have only a small, rather unimpressive entry hole, but quite a lot of damage deeper inside). Most are fairly easily treated by resting the person, placing pressure on the wound and if possible raising the cut part higher than the rest of the body. Remember the body has some very good ways of stopping bleeding on its own, so if a clot forms try not to disturb it.

Cannon balls were at least big enough to see and did not get lost in the body. A more modern problem associated with wounds and bleeding is that low velocity bullets tend to zig-zag through flesh, and do not necessarily go straight through. When someone has been shot and wounded the doctors need to know if there are any bullets left inside the body. It is important not to miss any. What I'm going to tell you is a very useful tip, and although you may never need to use it, it's a very interesting mathematical idea.

If someone has been shot, count the number of bullet holes. This will give you the highest number of bullets that could possibly still be inside. If there is an even number (2,4,6,8 and so on) there will be an even number of bullets inside – or none. If there is an odd number (1,3,5,7 and so on) there will be an odd number of bullets inside and definitely at least one.

This rule can be a help when looking for hidden injury with X-rays. A sad fact of the world at the moment is that the increased use of low velocity hand guns is making this problem more common. (High-powered guns are just as dangerous but bullets tend to go straight through the body.) The one thing to remember for the theory to hold up is that two bullets must not have passed through the same hole, or

gone in or out through a natural hole like the mouth.
Think about it. It's something I hope you'll never
need to use. Whatever else, it will make you more

logical and help your maths.

First aid is always improving and looking for new ideas like this which may help improve the chance of a casualty making a good recovery. Treatment has certainly got better since the Battle of Waterloo, where many men died because of poor first aid. One man was hit by a cannon ball which took both his arms off above the elbow. He bled to death after being allowed to walk several kilometres to get help.

Because of cannon ball and other injuries about 500 amputations had to be carried out during the battle. Fortunately the men were incredibly brave. The Marquis of Anglesey had to have his leg cut off, and when it was done he told his surgeon that the knife was blunt. Another patient who lost a limb was Lord Fitzroy Somerset. He called for his arm to be brought back after amputation as he had forgotten to take off his signet ring.

How should you get a blood-sucking leech off your body?

When I've been in the jungle I've found the best way is to put salt on the leech. If you try pulling it, its body may come off and leave the head attached to your skin. This can cause infection, like when a thorn is left stuck in your finger.

First, a general word about leeches, because they are fascinating creatures. I love them and I don't mind admitting it. Some leeches live on land, some in water. It's the land leeches you are most likely to meet, especially if you walk with bare ankles through the damp rain forests of South-East Asia.

They seem to have an uncanny knack of being able to see a meal coming. They attach themselves to bare flesh with amazing speed. Often the first you know about it is when you see your own blood running down your legs! They inject not only their very own anaesthetic which stops you feeling any pain, but also a substance to stop their meal clotting so they can eat more of it. The best way to avoid land leeches is to wear something to protect your lower legs: good shoes, trousers, and thick socks (just what you always wanted to wear in the heat of a tropical rain forest). Covering your legs with repellents will also help, but some leeches will still get through for lunch, though.

As I say, if they do attach themselves, I think the best way to get them off is with salt. Another method travellers have used is to cover them with vinegar or alcohol. If you have it, industrial spirit dabbed on is quite good. Burning them with a hot needle, a lighted match or cigarette has also been recommended in the past. Do not do this. You are likely to do more harm to yourself than to the leeches. You can try a sort of a scrape-flip action with your thumbnail, almost as though you are flipping the top off a bottle of pop. You have to be quick or they will just latch on to your thumb. I once put my feet into a bowl of leeches to show how they bite, on a live television programme. There were about a dozen of them in a tank. At the beginning of the interview we were worried that they might let us down and not attach themselves to me. (We did not feed them for a day or two before.) But by the end of the interview I was in a hopeless state. As fast as I got one off, either it or a friend would attach itself somewhere else on my body.

I had heard incredible stories about leeches that

live in water, in particular that they can crawl into various parts of the body while you are having a quiet dip in some far eastern forest pool. Some people have doubted if this really happens, so I wrote to one expert to find out. He replied that he had seen for himself a case where a big buffalo leech lived inside someone who had been swimming! And I know of cases where smaller leeches were found living in the back of the throat after they had got in hidden in dirty drinking water.

It must be said that leeches have always been useful to doctors. (Someone skilled in medicine used to be called a "leech". And this word itself comes from an old English one "laece", meaning someone who relieves pain, which, in turn, comes from the word "lacnian" to heal.) Leeches were used to suck blood out of sick people to try to make them better. Although this is not thought to be so helpful any more, there are some conditions, mainly of the lungs, where the blood gets too thick. The doctor may then have to draw some off to thin it. So we shouldn't be too dismissive of this old remedy.

Leeches have come a long way since those days, and are now being used in some of the latest surgery. Let's say a finger gets cut off accidentally. Surgeons may now be able to sew it back. But joining the very small blood vessels has always been the difficult part of the operation. For a few days the fate of the finger hangs in the balance. Swelling can easily undo all the surgeon's good work.

This is where the leech comes in. The surgeon lets it attach itself to the part of the finger that has been sewn back on. Not only will it suck away the unwanted swelling, but also the substance that the leech injects to stop a person's blood clotting – the stuff that makes your blood run down your legs

67

when you're bitten in the rain forest – will help the finger heal without a damaging clot forming. In this way the leech buys the surgeon time in the first few precious days when there is the wait to see if the piece of finger will grow back on.

A final true story about leeches shows how well they can adapt to new situations. After this TV programme I was telling you about, someone was going to throw our leeches down the toilet. (In fact we all thought this was rather cruel and we let them go in a canal outside the studio.) However, we were warned off even thinking about this because of something which actually happened at another nearby London TV studio. After an afternoon programme about leeches, the live animals were thrown down the toilet pan. Not very long after, a large security guard went in to use this toilet. He sat down and made himself comfortable with a newspaper.

When he got up he couldn't believe his eyes, but hanging painlessly all around his most sensitive parts were the "worms" which had climbed silently back up the pan.

He pulled his trousers on in a panic and ran off to the first aid room. As it happens this particular TV studio has two of these rooms, but only one nurse. On this day the spare first aid room was being used by a new secretary.

Our friend burst in expecting to find the nurse, and dropped his trousers – "What do you think of this?" She didn't think a lot from what I heard, and threw her typewriter at him before running out of the building, screaming.

That's the sort of tale that gives rise to the expression "stick like a leech"! And I can tell you they really do, whether you are in a London television studio toilet or a jungle in Nepal.

What should you do if you are sinking in mud or a quicksand?

T here are various things you can try. One book which was written by a soldier suggested "swimming" to safety. The idea was that you used the breast stroke – this has the advantage of spreading your body weight, and it slows you sinking. Another book recommends lying back and spreading your arms and legs. If your hands touch anything firm then you grab it. The best thing is not to get stuck in the first place. If you ever have to cross a swamp, tread carefully and step on to firm ground – there will often be small tufts of grass that will give some support.

And if you do get stuck, you could try following some other advice I've come across, and that is to "roll" out of the place. But only tell your Mum I suggested this if you really have to do it to save your life. I can remember one of the most dangerous things about falling into mud was going home with dirty clothes ...

Can you get epileptic fits from sitting too close to a TV?

Yes, it can happen (everyone seems to have heard of this), but it is very rare, and only affects a few people sensitive to this form of light. I doubt if many doctors have ever seen it. And it is important to understand that most fits do not have a cause like this. In fact the whole business of "fits" in children is rather complicated because of the way some grown-ups confuse words like this. "Black-outs", "convulsions", "absences" and "seizures" are just some of the other words they use not only for epilepsy, but also for many similar attacks. A common cause of a "convulsion" or "fit" in the very young is having a high temperature. This shouldn't be confused with epilepsy.

But back to the question, a very few people may have problems if they sit close to a TV set. Usually the room is dim and the set is being adjusted. The flickering light triggers the brain to have a fit, which is an unexpected burst of electricity from the brain to the body. A similar thing can happen to some car drivers who are travelling down a long straight road with tall trees growing on the side. If the trees are evenly spaced and the sun is shining through from behind, then a light pattern similar to the TV set is created. For some reason flashing disco lights seem to be much less of a problem. This is probably because they do not flash regularly and at the "right" rate.

But flashing lights are not the only things that can set off a fit. In 1931 it was discovered that certain music could do it – Tchaikovsky's "Waltz of the Flowers" to be precise. And it has also happened with

70

church bells and whistling kettles. Sometimes laughter can start things going. This is not at all funny as this type of fit is very dangerous, and the victim can literally die laughing. (I'm telling you this because it's interesting, not because you will ever see it happen. Most people who have epilepsy just have an occasional fit and otherwise lead perfectly normal lives.)

A major epileptic fit has four stages to it. The whole business may only last a few minutes. First the person may get a warning feeling that something is about to happen. The second stage involves the sufferer falling to the ground, often letting out a cry, and then going rigid for a few seconds. I think this stage is the most frightening for someone watching, because the neck and face go blue. The actual convulsions come in the third stage. Muscles contract violently. Then they relax. The jaw muscles clench the mouth tightly shut. This may make the breathing noisy and the tongue may get bitten. In the fourth stage the person relaxes and then comes round gradually, basically well but often dazed and not sure what has happened.

It is worth knowing what to do if this happens to a friend of yours. The most important thing is to stop your friend coming to any harm during the actual fit. So, say it happens in the classroom, you would move things such as chairs and desks away. If there is a fire near by it is vital not to let your friend fall on to it – there is no need to do this by force as someone having a fit is not aware of what's going on and can be easily guided. After that get help from an adult.

There are a few other things you can do to help. The best place to learn these is in a practical first aid class. One thing a lot of people think they must do is to force the person's mouth open. The idea behind

71

this is that it stops the tongue being bitten, but these days first aid experts recommend that you shouldn't try to put anything in the mouth – if you use force you may break some teeth or get your finger bitten.

So that is an outline of a typical major epileptic fit, and what to do when one happens. You are bound to see one at some time or other. If you are epileptic, do not feel "different" from everyone else. It is just an illness like any other. Some people are asthmatic, some get migraine headaches – we are all going to have some problems during our lives, and they can usually be helped with treatment. When people feel they are sicker than they really are, this can cause more trouble than the actual illness.

A final quick word about the way quite a lot of us "jump" when we are falling asleep. This is not a fit. No one really knows why this happens. The best idea I have heard is that it comes from the time millions of years ago when our distant relatives lived in trees like monkeys and apes. As they dropped off to sleep they would wake up with a jerk to stop themselves dropping off the branch. Some of us still have this reflex deep in our subconscious mind! It's a nice idea, anyway, whether it's true or not.

If you fall over, how do you know if you've broken a leg?

There are 206 bones in the body. Four of these are in each leg. One is the knee cap. The other three are the long bones.

If you break one of these long bones (either the one above the knee or the two below it) you may see it sticking through the skin. This sort of fracture is serious because dirt can get into the wound. This is one reason why it's so important not to move a fracture without great care. A simple break can be turned into a worse injury if a sharp broken bone end cuts through the skin. Being able to see the bone does make it very easy to know you have a break. People do not find this much comfort, though, when it actually happens to them.

But how do you decide if you can't see the bone? With some difficulty, is the answer, unless you have X-ray vision! And it's worth remembering that a break may not even show up on an X-ray. However, here are some things to think about if someone falls over and you don't know whether a bone has been broken.

A break is probably going to be painful, although this is not a sure sign, as a bad bruise can be painful too. Also some fractures are not painful – for example, if an old person falls over and breaks a hip, there may be no pain at all. Swelling is something else that's usually present. But again, a painful bruise can swell.

One particularly tell-tale sign is that an injured person tends not to use or move a broken part. This is a more useful general rule. You do not, for example, tend to run around on a broken leg. Also, if a limb is broken it may look peculiar. It may stick out at a funny angle, or be shorter than the one on the other side. Or it may move in an unusual way, perhaps flapping about like a bird's broken wing.

A sign to listen for is when two broken ends of a bone grate together like the edges of a broken cream cracker. (Do not deliberately move a leg to test for this. It may make things worse. It's also very painful and a very good way to lose a friend.)

These hints don't apply to all the other 198 bones. A broken skull may feel like the top of a hard-boiled egg that's been hit with a spoon. And if it's only cracked, like a plate of glass, then the damage may be impossible to see without an X-ray.

Some bones are hardly ever broken. The three smallest bones in the body, right inside the ear, are in a very well-protected position. Their main work is to help carry sound to the brain. But most bones of the skeleton are there to act as the framework on which the rest of the body is hung. They are like internal scaffolding. And although they can break, they are in fact very strong. The shin bones can support over 1,500 kilograms. In this they are rather better than solid steel rods.

It's interesting that children's bones do not break in the same way as adults'. In grown-ups the long bones snap like dry sticks. In children they may simply bend like a green stick or an archer's bow. A child's spine is so springy that it hardly ever breaks. And the pelvis is so tough that a car can run over it without damaging it as it would an adult's – though I am not recommending anybody to try this.

Young bones really are remarkable. Another important difference is in how amazingly well they heal. Broken bone ends will grow towards one another to reunite. In a grown-up doctors would

74

have to think about fixing them with steel pins. Also, if a break results in one of a child's legs becoming shorter than the other, nature seems to be able to correct this on its own. In adults weights may have to be used to stop the leg shortening. You've probably seen pictures of these weights hanging from the ends of hospital beds.

The younger you are when a break occurs the better all this natural healing tends to be. Some fractures may still need very careful attention, for example those at the elbow, because nearby nerves and blood vessels could be easily damaged. But usually once a fracture stops hurting and you are up and about you should be able to go back to school and show off your plaster!

What should you do if someone has a broken neck?

I t is very important that you do not move any fracture as this may make the damage worse. And it is especially so when it's the spine that's broken. The reason is that this backbone (which includes the neck) has the spinal cord running through it like a white thread through some beads. The 24 "beads" (or vertebrae) are in this case tied firmly together by tough fibres. But if the bones are broken or become free to move about then the "thread" running through them can break too. If this happens serious problems develop. Quite what, depends on where the damage is. (The nearer the head, the worse things usually are.) The vertebrae are different shapes but the basic design is a bony "body" with the hole for the spinal cord. Each "body" has various spines sticking out of it. As a matter of interest, the longest spine is on the seventh vertebra in the neck. (You have the same number of vertebrae in your neck as a giraffe!) The vertebrae are numbered from the top, and you can feel your own seventh as a lump in the back of the neck just below the neck of a T-shirt.

The spinal cord itself is a soft white piece of nerve that looks like a rope. It is on average 45 centimetres long and is the main motorway of messages between the brain and the rest of the body. At the bottom end – at about the level of your lower back – it splays out like a frayed rope. It is quite soft and easily damaged, and once this happens it is impossible to repair. So it must be protected. The spine does this very well – as long as it is firm and unbroken, it is very strong (its strength is the main reason why your head stays on the top of your body).

If there is back pain or if there has been a fall or a

blow to the spine be particularly careful with an injured person. The most common break is low down, about where a belt crosses your back. What usually causes this is a fall from a height, landing either on the feet or bottom, or a heavy weight falling on to the shoulders. The sudden jerk forward in a car accident will damage the higher part of the spine, in the neck. Also, in young people a common cause of fracture of the neck is diving into water which is not deep enough. Never dive into water where you cannot see the bottom or are uncertain of the depth. In other words, make sure you know which is the shallow end of the pool before you dive in. A special collar can be put on to keep a broken neck firm. And often you will see trained ambulance men lifting an injured person on to a stretcher very carefully, keeping the body as still as possible. Spinal damage is the main reason for them doing this.

When I was at school our gymnastics team was in a bad car accident. The master in charge broke his neck. One of the team (he is now a famous doctor) saved the gym master's life by supporting the neck until help arrived. He recovered very well in hospital and went on for years making my life a misery on parallel bars and trampolines.

How could you protect yourself from a gigantic golden eagle if you were only carrying a Hamlyn encyclopaedia?★

Have no fear. You probably don't even need a thick book. Although there is a famous thriller called *The Birds* in which crows and gulls terrorise people, in real life our feathered friends tend not to attack humans. Most accidents come when people hold birds. Those – like storks – with long necks and sharp pointed beaks are particularly dangerous. So too can be birds of prey whose talons can easily rip out an eye. So beware of these. Keep trouble at arm's length.

You sometimes read stories about eagles carrying off babies to eat. I doubt if things like this do happen. Anyone who has tried to take a picture of an eagle will know how difficult it is even to get near them. On the other hand, anyone who raids a nest is asking for anything that the mother eagle can dish out.

It is sensible as well as kind to leave wild birds' nests alone. Quite a few people have ended up with broken arms after messing about with nesting swans. One angler, no featherweight at over 120 kilograms, had his boat overturned when he annoyed one. They may only weigh 10-12 kilograms themselves but they can easily knock over wind surfers or water skiers who stray into their territory.

Ostriches can give you a good kick. And there have been lots of reports of this happening. The male ostrich is supposed to be particularly nasty when out looking for a girlfriend. As a matter of interest, if you are ever set on by stroppy ostriches the recom-

★ *Editor's note*   Yes, Dr Pete was actually asked this!

mended way out of trouble is to lie down flat on your face. This comes close to burying your head in the sand, as the saying goes, but I am told they will then leave you alone. I've never had to try it. I suppose it's worth knowing in case they do set on you and you are without a Hamlyn encyclopaedia!

If you are shipwrecked in an open boat, what happens if you drink sea water?

To understand what happens when you drink any sort of water, you really need to understand why you feel thirsty in the first place.

Two parts of the body keep watch on the water inside you. First, there are special brain cells deep inside your skull. If they think they're getting dry, they send a message to let you know it's time to have a drink. Second, the chest plays a part in sending these sorts of messages. The large blood vessels there take blood to and from the heart. If there is less blood than normal, due to a shortage of water in the body (remember blood is over 99 per cent water), sensitive nerve endings in the walls of the blood vessels detect that they are, literally, not at full stretch. This very clever system can be fooled by going into space. One experiment in Skylab showed that weightlessness in space stopped astronauts feeling thirsty – their bodies were confused by there being no outside pressure pushing in on the chest.

You can't get rid of the feeling of thirst just by having water in your mouth, even though when you're thirsty this may be dry. Fluid needs to get right into you. In fact you do not even need to drink it. A dry mouth can be relieved by fluid being put directly into your blood.

Thirst can become a desperate urge if you have nothing to drink. People have stayed alive for months without food. But you can only last a few days without water. (The record for staying alive without both is 18 days. This happened in 1979 in Austria when a man who had been a passenger in a car crash was locked in police cells and forgotten.)

If you are lucky and have some fresh drinking water in your lifeboat when you are shipwrecked, it will go straight across the stomach wall and into the circulation without any problem at all. This increases the amount of blood. Then the two kidneys which are filtering the blood all the time will start to make urine out of what you have drunk.

It's important that they do this because this is how the body gets rid of a lot of waste. In an average day on land you will produce about 1.5 litres of urine. If you could see the solid part that's dissolved in this, there would be about 50 grammes. About 30 grammes are urea – the poisonous waste substance left after the breakdown of food – and then there are 15 grammes of salt. If the kidneys stop working this waste and salt collects and will kill you. (People whose own kidneys are not working properly may have to go on to artificial kidney machines to filter out the poisons and stop this happening. Sometimes it may be possible to transplant healthy kidneys to replace those which have failed.)

Anyway, you have your drink and some hours later this shows up as urine. The two kidneys can help save water if you are short of it, so how much urine is made depends on how dry you are. You may have noticed that urine is a dark colour on hot days in the summer. This is because it's concentrated. Fluid is being lost as sweat and there is less available to make urine.

To stay alive you must make at least 300 millilitres of urine a day – this amount, which would about half fill a standard milk bottle, is the minimum necessary to carry the body's waste away. But if thirst drives you to drink sea water the kidneys, which are making salty urine anyway, have great difficulty handling the extra salt in it. This then starts to build up in the

blood. (Incidentally, you can see that however desperate you become, it's no good drinking your own
urine. It's the body's own homemade poisonous

water.) As the blood gets more salty it tends to suck water out of the rest of the body. The power of the salty blood to draw water from the body is the same power that roots of trees use to pull water out of the ground and to take it up many metres to the leaves.

Over the days you drink sea water, your blood sucks its own brain dry like this. As the cells inside your head shrink, you go literally stark raving mad. Hence the famous cry of the Ancient Mariner: "Water, water, every where, nor any drop to drink." However, thirst is such a powerful feeling that castaways are often tempted to this slow death.

Other animals' kidneys often work in a different way from ours. Much depends on where they live. Animals that actually live in sea water have had to develop ways of dealing with the salt. Fish such as the dogfish are able to survive quite happily in the sea because their blood can handle high levels of chemicals which would kill us. Some fish have to be really clever. Salmon and eels migrate and spend part of their lives in fresh water and part in sea water. One way the eel manages to do this is by making more urine in fresh water than when it's in the sea.

Back on land, the kangaroo rat of North American deserts lives where there is very little drinking water. Some books say it never actually drinks, but just takes in a little water in food. It survives very nicely because its kidneys can make a much more concentrated urine than ours. It wastes no water at all. I've never heard of anyone being shipwrecked with a North American kangaroo rat, but it would be a great companion if you were. You could have nearly all the water. It would be quite happy living on next to none.

Why should you "Never Shave a Camel"?

For the same reason that you should not tickle a moray eel under the chin! I saw the finger of a man who did this off the Atlantic island of Ascension. It had 16 stitches in it. Camels can be really grumpy – especially in the mating season – but even a cheerful one is likely to object to a shave. And their hooked teeth can give a very nasty bite.

Another reason is that it would be very cruel. It has been worked out that if you shave a camel it could double the animal's water loss into the desert air. This could kill it.

The camel can live in places like the Sahara because it is very good at controlling water going in and out of its body. If it doesn't get enough to drink it can make some out of the fat in its humps. With one hump or two, a camel can go over two weeks without drinking water. Then when it does get some, it can guzzle over 90 litres in a few minutes, to top itself up.

It's all very well the camel being able to fill up like this, but it's no good if the water immediately evaporates into the hot air as fast as it can drink. To help stop water loss from the skin, camels have hairy coats. The nomads who ride the camels wear long flowing robes and have vests for the same reason – not to keep warm, but to trap air around their bodies, because this protects the skin from the hot dry desert air.

The camel has been around millions of years learning how best to live happily in the desert. If you do start to meddle with it, or with anything in the natural world, you can do a lot of harm. So Never Shave a Camel!

Some first aid words, what they mean and where to find out more about them in the book

Airway   38–43, 58–9
Air goes into the body through the mouth and nose. It goes down into the lungs through a passage called the airway.

Artificial resuscitation   42–3
This is a procedure you can learn which may help you save the life of someone whose heart beat or breathing has stopped. It involves restarting the heart and getting air into the lungs.

Bite   10–13, 16–24, 44–7, 49, 65–8, 84
To wound with teeth (or with mouth, as insects do).

Black out   70–1
Sudden loss of consciousness. There are a number of causes, of which an epileptic fit is one.

Bleeding   60–3
Loss of blood either externally through the skin or internally into body tissues and spaces.

Burn   25, 29–30
Damage to the body by extremes of temperature (heat or cold), or by chemicals, electricity or friction (for example, when sliding down a rope).

Cardiac arrest   54–8
When the heart beat stops.

Choke   54, 58–9
When there is a blockage of the airway so that air

cannot get in and out of the lungs.

Death 38–43, 54–8
The end of life. Some parts of the body die more quickly than others. The most important area, the brain, dies quickly if cut off from blood and oxygen, and cannot recover as other parts can. When this happens, a person is said to be "dead".

Dehydration 80–4
When the body lacks water.

Fracture 73–7
A break, crack or bend in a bone.

Heat exhaustion 33
When a person slowly becomes very tired, feeling sick and faint, because the body has lost salt and water through sweating which have not been replaced.

Heat stroke 32–3
When the body temperature rises uncontrollably in the heat, often because the person is not sweating normally to cool down.

Hypothermia 34–5
When there is a dangerous lowering of the body temperature.

Hysteria 18
A temporary state of mind when a person loses control of emotions and feelings, often as a result of fright. Quite what happens varies, but the person often shouts, cries or screams, and may roll about on the ground.

Kiss of life 42–3
The mouth-to-mouth action of blowing air into the lungs of someone who has stopped breathing. Part of artificial resuscitation.

Poison 10–13, 18–21, 47–8
A substance which if taken into the body even in small amounts can kill or damage health.

Recovery position 58
A comfortable lying position in which an unconscious person can be left face-down to recover without choking.

Shock 24–9, 62
Although it has other everyday meanings, in first aid this is when the blood fails to reach some areas of the body. There are a lot of causes, ranging from bleeding to the sorts of "shock" that you might immediately think of, like an electric shock or the shock of seeing something unpleasant.

Sting 47–8, 52–3
A wound caused by a sharp-pointed part of an animal or plant where poison is injected. There is often a poison gland attached to the sting.

Venom 10–13, 18–21, 47–8
A poison delivered by a bite or sting.

First aid classes

Three voluntary organisations, St John Ambulance, St Andrew's Ambulance Association and the British Red Cross Society, all run first aid courses in Britain. Why not find out about local classes? You can use the telephone book or the Yellow Pages to find the phone number of a group in your area.